Edwin

by

Roslyn Schwartz

DUMA
GRAD
CITY OF WORDS

Dumagrad: A City of Words
Toronto, Canada
wordcity.ca

Distribution:
Books In Hand
A division of LitDistCo
ordering@litdistco.ca
8300 Lawson Rd.
Milton, ON L9T 0A4

ISBN 978-1-988887-04-3

Library and Archives Canada Cataloguing in Publication

Title: Edwin / Roslyn Schwartz.
Names: Schwartz, Roslyn, 1951- author, illustrator.
Identifiers: Canadiana 20190164859 | ISBN 9781988887043 (hardcover)
Classification: LCC PS8587.C5785 E39 2019 | DDC C813/.54—dc23

Printed in Canada
10 9 8 7 6 5 4 3 2 1

Hello

My name
is
Edwin

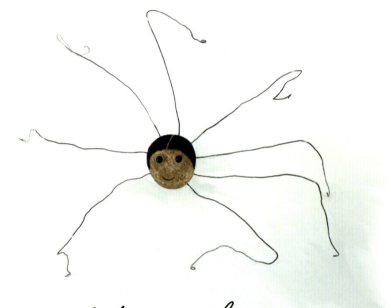

I have legs

And I have feelings

This is not what I thought
my life would be like

I thought I would be young forever

And I nearly was

Then I got old

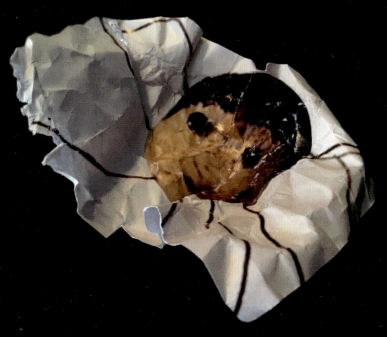

Old enough to die

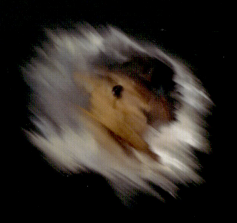

Sigh.

But for now

I am alive

My name is Edwin

I have legs

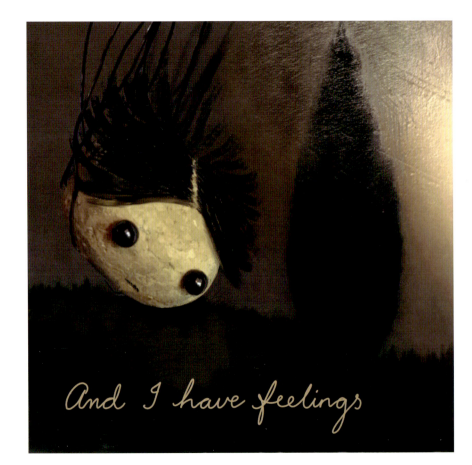

And I have feelings

This is <u>not</u> what I thought
my life <u>would</u> be like

And I nearly was

Old enough to die

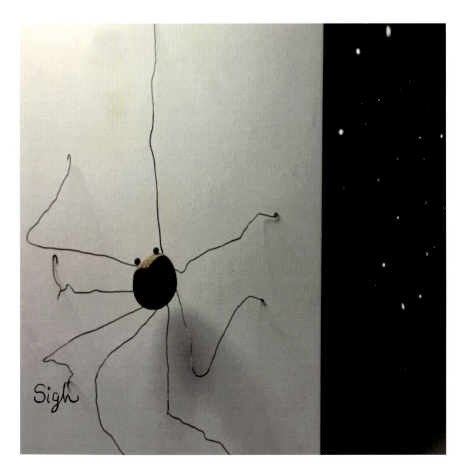

But
For
Now

I am alive.

ART

And I have feelings.

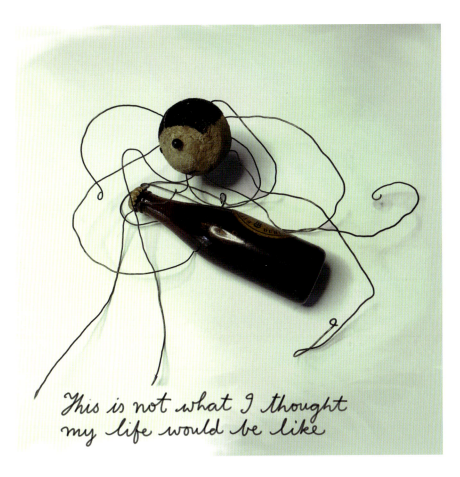

This is not what I thought
my life would be like

I thought I would be young forever.

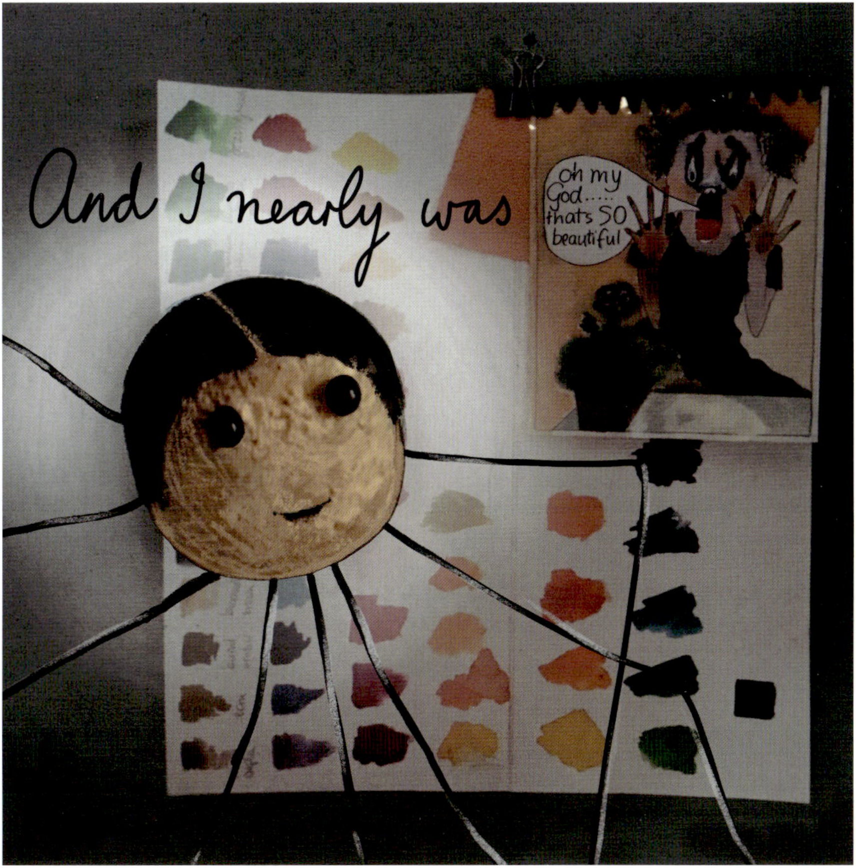
And I nearly was
oh my God..... thats SO beautiful

Then I got old

But for now

I am alive

Hello

My name is

Edwin

I have legs

And I have feelings

I'm depressed

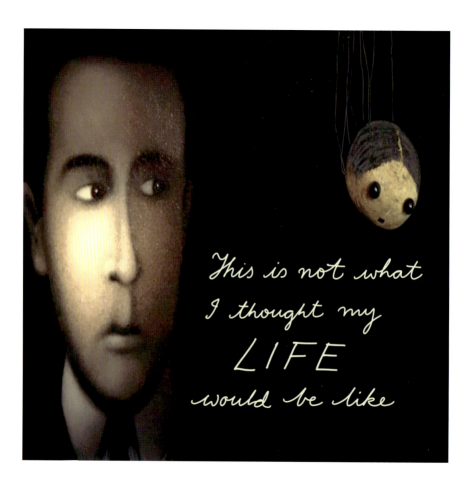

I thought I would be young forever

And I nearly was

Old enough to die

Sigh

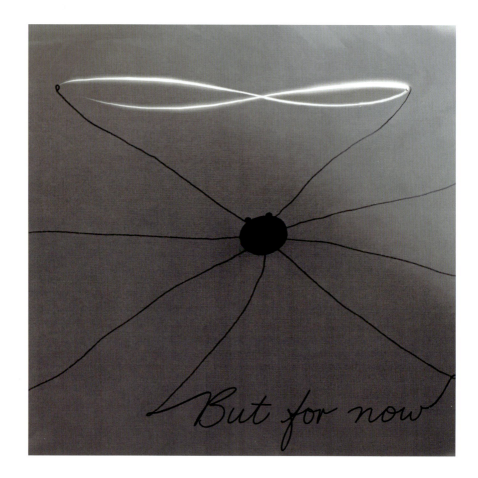

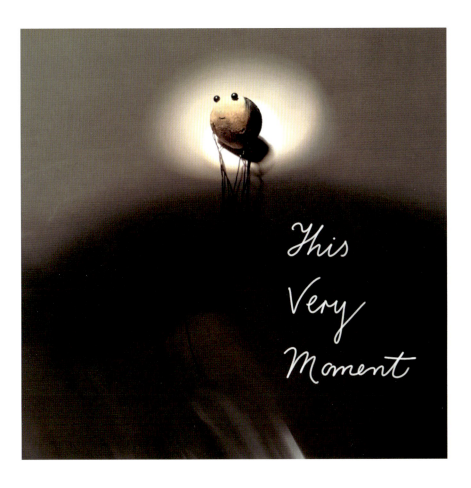

This
Very
Moment

I am alive

Roslyn Schwartz was born in Montreal and grew up in Tunbridge Wells, Kent, England.

She is best known for *The Mole Sisters*, a series of picture books for which she was awarded the Writer's Trust Vicky Metcalf Award for Literature for Children.

Edwin is her first picture book for adults.

Edwin was made possible with help from the estate of JOHN GRIFFIN b. 1948 — d. 2015.